Letts
and
LONSDALE

KS2
Success
Workbook

Lynn Huggins-Cooper

Science
SATs

Contents

Plants

Animals and ecosystems

Humans

Materials

Physical processes

National Test practice

Answers

See additional answer booklet

Parts of a flowering plant

Parts of a flowering plant

Match the labels to the correct part of the plant.

root

petal

stem

leaf

1

2

3

4

Missing words

Fill in the missing words using the words in the box below.

The **1** ＿＿＿＿＿＿ carries water and **2** ＿＿＿＿＿＿ from the soil to the plant, and keeps it **3** ＿＿＿＿＿＿ in the ground. The **4** ＿＿＿＿＿＿ are often brightly coloured and scented to attract insects. The **5** ＿＿＿＿＿ act as 'food factories' using the **6** ＿＿＿＿＿ from sunlight.

| energy | nutrients | root | leaves | petals | anchored |

Quick questions!

1 Name two ways in which petals may attract insects to flowers.

＿＿＿＿＿＿＿＿＿＿＿＿＿＿＿＿＿＿＿＿＿＿＿＿＿＿＿＿

2 Name the two functions of a root. ＿＿＿＿＿＿＿＿＿＿

＿＿＿＿＿＿＿＿＿＿＿＿＿＿＿＿＿＿＿＿＿＿＿＿＿＿＿＿

＿＿＿＿＿＿＿＿＿＿＿＿＿＿＿＿＿＿＿＿＿＿＿＿＿＿＿＿

3 Which part of a plant makes food using sunlight?

＿＿＿＿＿＿＿＿＿＿＿＿＿＿＿＿＿＿＿＿＿＿＿＿＿＿＿＿

What is inside a flower?

Match the labels to the correct internal part of a flower. Use the words in the box below.

anther

stamen

stigma

ovule

ovary

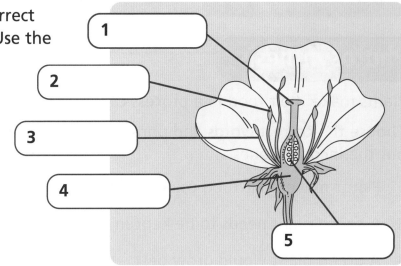

1

2

3

4

5

Functions

Match the parts of the flower to the function (what it is that they do for the flower) by writing the numbers in the boxes.

1 stamen   **2** ovary   **3** anther   **4** stigma

☐ **a** holds the pollen

☐ **b** where the pollen enters the female part of the flower

☐ **c** the stick that holds the anthers in the air

☐ **d** where the ovules are stored

Top Tip *Make a set of cards with the name of the plant part on one side and write the function on the other side. Use them to test yourself and you will soon be an expert!*

I never knew flowers were so complicated!

I just thought they smelt nice...

Photosynthesis

Photosynthesis

Plants make their food in a process called **photosynthesis**.

Choose the correct words and phrases to complete the sentences by crossing out the incorrect ones.

1 Plants make their food using the energy from *sunlight / a battery* .

2 A green plant needs to be kept in the *light / dark* to grow properly.

3 A green plant would grow best *on a windowsill / in a cupboard* .

What do plants need to grow?

Match the labels to the correct plant.

1 grown without sufficient light, but enough water ☐

2 grown with sufficient light and water ☐

3 grown with enough light, but not enough water ☐

A   B   C

See how they grow!

1 Name three things a plant needs to grow healthily.

_____

2 What would happen to a plant that was not watered?

_____

3 What would happen to a plant grown next to a window in a dimly lit room?

_____

4 What is the green-coloured chemical called that is found in leaves, and helps plants to make their own food using the energy from the sun?

_____

What happens to plants grown in the dark?

Fill in the gaps using the words from the box below.

If you put plants in the dark, they turn **1** _____. They need the
2 _____ from the **3** _____ to make their food. There is a
special green chemical in their **4** _____ called **5** _____
that helps them to do this.

> light energy   leaves   yellow   chlorophyll   Sun

Quick questions

1 Circle the things in this list that plants need to grow healthily.

> **a** water   **b** soil   **c** quiet   **d** light   **e** fertiliser

2 If a plant was growing bent over, towards the light, how could you make
it grow straight again? Why would your idea work?

_____

_____

3 What is the name of the process plants use to make their own food using
energy from the Sun?

_____

Top Tip *Remember, 'synthesis' means 'made' and 'photo' means 'light' – so photosynthesis means 'made using light'!*

So remember – plants are like small children – they don't like the dark!

It's not the dark I don't like – it's what might be lurking in the dark...

Seeds and germination

What makes a seed germinate?

Choose the sentence that best describes what a seed needs to germinate.

1   A seed needs air and the correct temperature to germinate, or start to grow.

2   A seed needs moisture, air and the correct temperature to germinate, or start to grow.

3   A seed needs moisture to germinate, or start to grow.

4   A seed needs the correct temperature to germinate, or start to grow.

Missing words

Fill in the gaps using words from the box below.

1 _____ sticks to the 2 _____. The male
3 _____ in the pollen travel down a 4 _____ into the
5 _____ of the plant and join the 6 _____ cells in the
7 _____. This is how 8 _____ are produced.

| ovary | seeds | stigma | cells | female | ovules | tube | pollen |

How is a plant pollinated?

Choose the best words and circle them.

Once a plant has grown and produced   **1** *leaves / flowers* , it may be
pollinated. This means that the pollen from the anthers of another
2 *plant / creature*   of the same type has landed on the   **3** *male / female*
parts of the plant. The female part of the plant, called the
4 *stigma / stamen* , is sticky.

The pollen may be carried on the wind or by   **5** *insects / cats* . Once the
pollen has landed on the stigma of a plant, it travels down a tube and
fertilises the   **6** *ovules / ovulation* . The fertilised ovules will become
7 *seeds / pollen* .

Plant life cycles

Put these words into the correct order to describe the life cycle of a plant. Write a sentence to explain each word.

a pollination **b** germination **c** fertilisation **d** seed dispersal

1 _____

2 _____

3 _____

4 _____

Quick questions

1 Name two ways in which pollen is carried from one plant to another.

_____

2 Name four ways in which seeds are dispersed.

_____

3 Describe the life cycle of a dandelion plant.

_____

4 What do seeds need in order to germinate?

_____

_____   **Top Tip** *Make a collection of seeds and think about how they are dispersed. Are most seeds spread in the same way?*

_____

So how are seeds spread when animals eat the fruit?

Think about it, stupid!

9

Plants investigation

How does water get to the parts of a plant?

What you need:

- A white carnation or white chrysanthemum

- An old plastic container to stand the flower in

- Food colouring – blue, green or purple are good colours to use

- Water

- A spoon

- Newspaper to cover surfaces

- An old shirt or apron

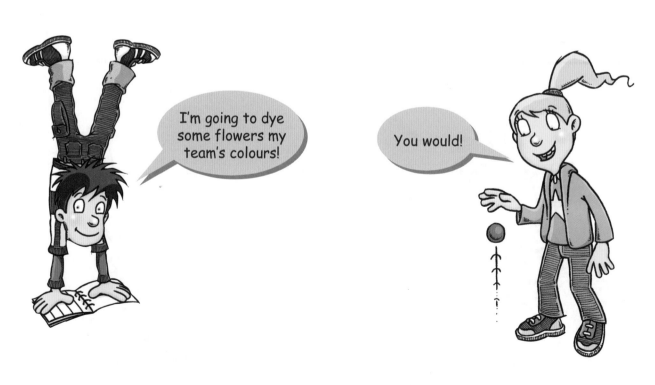

What to do

1   Half fill your container with water.

2   Add 12 drops of food colouring – do not drop it on your clothes because it will stain!

3   Stir the water to mix in the colouring.

4   Carefully stand your flower with the bottom of the stem in the coloured water.

5   Leave the flower in the water for a day. Check it every hour or so. What do you think will happen?

What you will see

The flower will suck the water up through the stem. This is what happens to all plants, but we cannot usually see the water. The white flower will stain the same colour as the food colouring you have chosen.

You can do this experiment with celery too. A stick of celery left standing in coloured water will suck up coloured water, and you will be able to see the 'pipes' in the stem!

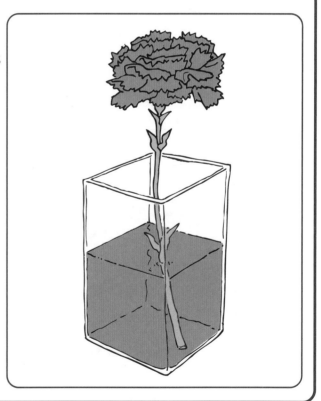

Sorting and classifying

Count the ways!

Look at the list of animals in the box. How many ways can you think of to sort them into groups?

cat   rabbit   snake   hen

turtle   whale   alligator   gerbil

parrot   crocodile   frog   seal

_____

_____

_____

Odd one out

Which of the creatures in each set is the odd one out?

Think about the characteristics of the animals.

1 dog/cat/rabbit   _____

2 snake/rabbit/hen   _____

3 fish/whale/mouse   _____

4 slug/snail/tortoise   _____

5 spider/ladybird/ground beetle   _____

Classification keys

Classification keys ask a series of simple questions to help you to sort things into groups. What questions could you ask yourself to design a key to sort the following plants and creatures?

crab   cat   butterfly   blackbird   lettuce   apple tree

_____

_____

_____

_____

_____

Sorting similar creatures

1 Canary or yellow brimstone butterfly? _____

I have wings. I have fewer than four legs. I am yellow. I have feathers. What am I?

2 Tabby cat or tiger? _____

I have fur. I have stripes. I have sharp teeth and hunt animals as prey. I am smaller than an Alsatian dog. What am I?

3 Ladybird or weevil? _____

I have six legs. I have two antennae. I am an insect. I eat aphids. I am red. What am I?

Who is in my gang?

Look at the list of animals below. Sort them into sets each time by answering the questions.

polar bear	lion	crocodile	zebra	whale
snake	turtle	giraffe	penguin	crab

1 Has fur. _____

Does not have fur. _____

2 Adapted to life in a cold place. _____

Not adapted to life in a cold place. _____

3 Lays eggs. _____

Does not lay eggs. _____

4 Has a shell. _____

Does not have a shell. _____

Practise classification by sorting piles of objects according to their characteristics. Can you sort the same pile using different criteria? You could sort them according to colour, what they are used for – anything you can think of!

I need to sort out my room...

Don't look at me – I'm off!

Food chains

Ordering food chains

Put these food chains in the right order.

1 sun   thrush   caterpillar   lettuce

_____

2 oystercatcher   sun   seaweed   periwinkle

_____

3 cat   sun   mouse   corn

_____

4 pondweed   tadpole   sun   duck

_____

Remember, all energy comes originally from the sun. Plants use sunlight to make their own food through a process called photosynthesis. Then animals eat the plants and other animals in turn eat those animals.

Spot the top carnivore!

If the top carnivore is a predator which is not eaten by any other creature, which is the top carnivore in each food chain? Put each food chain in the correct order and circle the top carnivore.

1 jaguar   monkey   plant buds   sun

_____

2 sun   fish   seaweed   seal   orca

_____

3 sun   slug   cat   blackbird   delphinium flower

_____

4 wolf   sun   deer   tree sapling

_____

Funny to think that a hedgehog is a fierce predator!

It's not very funny for the slugs in the garden.

Who is who?

Add the labels in the box below to the organisms (plants and animals) in the food chain.

1 sun ➜ dandelion ☐ snail ☐ thrush ☐ sparrowhawk ☐

2 sun ➜ primrose ☐ slug ☐ hedgehog ☐ fox ☐

a primary producer **b** primary consumer
c secondary consumer **d** tertiary consumer

Predator or prey?

In each set of animals below, two are prey (herbivores, who eat only plants) and one is a predator (a carnivore, who hunts and eats other animals). Which is the predator?

1 cat/gerbil/fieldmouse _____

2 deer/mountain lion/rabbit _____

3 crocodile/antelope/zebra _____

4 owl/mouse/rabbit _____

Missing words

Use the words in the box below to fill in the gaps.

A food chain is the simplest way of showing the way that **1** _____ is transferred from organism to organism. All energy comes originally from the **2** _____. Plants use sunlight to make their own food through a process called **3** _____. In a food chain, a plant is called a primary **4** _____, because it produces food for other creatures. An animal that eats plants is called a **5** _____. In a food chain, a herbivore is a **6** _____ consumer. Animals that eat other animals are called **7** _____. In a food chain, **8** _____ are called secondary, or even tertiary consumers.

carnivores   producer   sun   photosynthesis
predators   herbivore   energy   primary

Web of life

Choose the right word

Underline the best word in each case.

Creatures and **1** *plants / bears* living within a particular
2 *habitat / place* , such as a desert, are all linked in a great web of life. The animals **3** *compete / argue* with each other for food and only the strongest, best **4** *adapted / prepared* creatures survive and breed. If a particular creature in a food chain is wiped out due to disease, **5** *carnivores / herbivores* further up the food chain are affected. As there is less food, competition becomes **6** *harder / easier* .

Meanings mix-up!

Match the words to the correct meaning by writing numbers in the boxes.

1 ecology   **2** habitat   **3** ecosystem   **4** community

☐ **a** the place in which a collection of plants and animals live

☐ **b** the animals and plants that live together in a particular place

☐ **c** the scientific term that describes the community and its habitat

☐ **d** the study of the relationship between animals, plants and their surroundings

Quick questions

1 Name five habitats. _____

2 How is a penguin adapted to the cold?

_____

3 How is a crab adapted to life on the seashore?

_____

4 Why has the Peppered Moth that lives in the city developed dark wings and the Peppered Moth that lives in the countryside developed pale wings?

_____

5 Why does the Arctic Fox turn white in the winter?

_____

Plant life cycles

The circulatory system – quick questions

1 Which vessels carry blood away from the heart – veins or arteries?

_____

2 Which carry oxygenated blood – veins or arteries?

_____

3 Is it more dangerous to cut a vein or an artery? Why?

_____

4 What two things can you do to keep your heart healthy?

_____

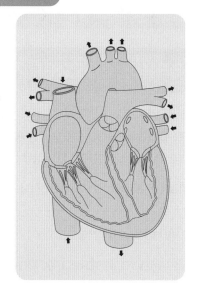

What is blood made up of?

Match the words to the descriptions by writing the numbers in the boxes.

We think of blood as a red liquid, but if you looked at blood under a strong microscope you would see several different things:

1 red cells (these look like red saucers)

2 white cells   **3** platelets   **4** plasma

☐ **a** This is the liquid that contains proteins, salts and sugars.

☐ **b** These attack invading microbes and fight disease.

☐ **c** These carry the dissolved oxygen around the body.

☐ **d** These are bits of dead cells. They gum together and help to clot your blood. When you cut yourself, they seal the wound to make a scab.

I'm off to run round the park – are you coming?

Only if we get ice-cream on the way home - we'll have earned it!

Humans investigation

Family dossier

Everybody knows that people have different fingerprints – we hear about it on police and detective programmes on the television. But it is interesting to see how similar fingerprints can be too!

Make a set of fingerprints for your family.

What you need:

- A washable ink pad (like the type you get with a stamping kit) OR washable poster colour paint

- Good quality plain paper such as drawing paper or the paper used by computer printers

- Willing family members – these can be hard to find!

- Soap and water for cleaning fingers afterwards

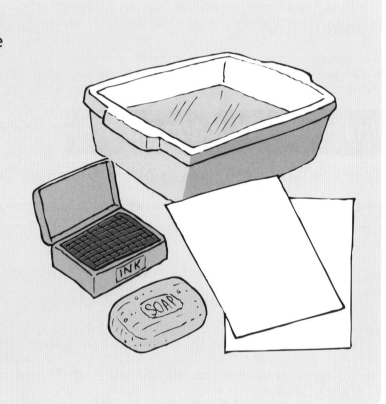

So, fingerprinting catches criminals...

I just hope Mum doesn't dust the biscuit barrel!

What to do

1   Get each person to ink their finger from the last joint to the end.

2   Ask each person to press their finger onto the paper, rolling it slowly and gently so that the whole fingerprint pattern appears on the paper.

3   Write the person's name on the sheet.

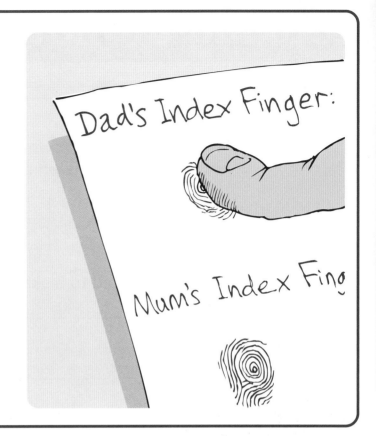

What to look for

Examine the patterns found on the fingerprints. You may see lines and creases as well as the circles or whorls on each print. Does anyone have similar fingerprints? Look closely at the lines and markings on people's hands. It is amazing to think how different and individual we all are!

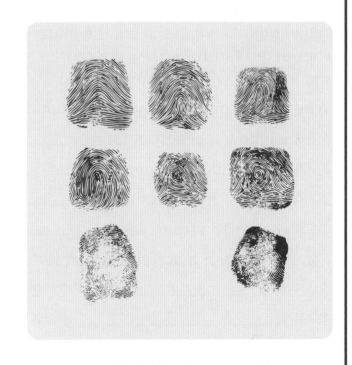

You can also look at other ways in which people are all different. Even within birth families (the families people are actually born into) there are many different characteristics. Look at eye colour, shape of features, shoe size, etc. It is amazing to think that in a world population of billions, we are all unique – even identical twins!

Looking at materials

Synthetic or natural?

1 Write an 'S' next to the materials which are synthetic (made by people) and an 'N' next to the materials which are natural (found in nature).

☐ **a** feather down   ☐ **b** wood   ☐ **c** plastic

☐ **d** polystyrene   ☐ **e** bone   ☐ **f** stone

2 What raw materials are used to make these objects?

a silk dress _____

b glass window _____

c wooden chair _____

d woollen jumper _____

Choosing materials

When objects are designed, the materials they are to be made from are considered carefully. They are chosen according to their characteristics and the job they will be required to do.

Why would these materials be unsuitable for the object described?

1 A window made from fabric. _____

2 A door made from paper. _____

3 A mattress made from stone. _____

4 A chair made from glass. _____

Can you suggest a better material for each item?

1 _____ **2** _____

3 _____ **4** _____

I've always fancied a paper dress, like they had in the 1960s...

Handy if you forgot your hankie!

Letts
and
LONSDALE

Answer Booklet

KS2 Science SATs

KS2
Success

Workbook
Answer
Booklet

Science
SATs

Plants

PAGES 4–5 PARTS OF A FLOWERING PLANT

Parts of a flowering plant

1 petal
2 root
3 leaf
4 stem

Missing words

1 root
2 nutrients
3 anchored
4 petals
5 leaves
6 energy

Quick questions!

1 scent, colour
2 to anchor the plant in the soil, draw up water and nutrients from the soil
3 leaves

What is inside a flower?

1 stigma
2 anther
3 stamen
4 ovary
5 ovule

Functions

a 3   b 4   c 3   d 2

PAGES 6–7 PHOTOSYNTHESIS

Photosynthesis

1 sunlight
2 light
3 on a windowsill

What do plants need to grow?

1 A   2 B   3 C

See how they grow!

1 correct temperature, water and light
2 It would wilt, then die.
3 It would bend towards the light.
4 chlorophyll

What happens to plants grown in the dark?

1 yellow
2 light energy
3 sun
4 leaves
5 chlorophyll

Quick questions

circled items are:

1 a, d (b – soil is important and should not be marked wrong, although plants can grow healthily without soil – stonecrops grow in walls and plants can be grown hydroponically).
2 Move the plant around so that it is bent away from the light. The stem will straighten as the plant seeks the light from the window.
3 photosynthesis

PAGES 8–9 SEEDS AND GERMINATION

What makes a seed germinate?

2 A seed needs moisture, air and the correct temperature to germinate, or start to grow.

Missing words

1 pollen
2 stigma
3 cells
4 tube
5 ovary
6 female
7 ovules
8 seeds

How is a plant pollinated?

1 flowers
2 plant
3 female
4 stigma
5 insects
6 ovules
7 seeds

Plant life cycles

a pollination – when pollen from one plant is introduced to another plant of the same species
c fertilisation – when the male cells from the pollen join with the female cells from the ovules
b germination – when a seed starts to sprout and grow
d seed dispersal – when seeds are broadcast or spread

Quick questions

1 wind, insects
2 explosion, carried on fur, eaten by and passed through animals and birds, carried by water, wind
3 Seed blows on wind, lands on soil and germinates, grows into plant, is pollinated, fertilised, seeds are dispersed on the wind and the cycle begins again.
4 correct temperature, moisture

Animals and ecosystems

PAGES 12–13 SORTING AND CLASSIFYING

Count the ways!

lives mostly in water: crocodile, frog, seal, turtle, whale

lays eggs: crocodile, frog, hen, snake, turtle

both categories: crocodile, frog, turtle

has fur: cat, rabbit, gerbil

does not have fur: snake, hen, alligator, parrot (or has feathers/does not have feathers, has scales/does not have scales)

mammal: cat, rabbit, gerbil

is not a mammal: parrot, snake, hen, alligator (or is/is not reptile/bird), or lays eggs/does not lay eggs, etc.

Odd one out

1 rabbit – it is a herbivore and the others are carnivores
2 rabbit – others lay eggs
3 mouse – does not live in water OR fish – mouse and whale are mammals
4 slug – others have shells OR tortoise – others are not reptiles
5 spider – has eight legs (and is an arachnid) and others have six legs (and are insects)

Classification keys

plant/animal, annual plant/woody plant, has fur/does not have fur, has shell/does not have shell, has wings/does not have wings, has feathers/does not have feathers

Sorting similar creatures

1 canary (fewer than 4 legs, feathers)
2 tabby cat (smaller than Alsatian)
3 ladybird (eats aphids, red)

Who is in my gang?

1 has fur: polar bear, lion; does not have fur: crocodile, zebra, whale, snake, turtle, giraffe, penguin, crab
2 adapted to life in a cold place: polar bear, penguin; not adapted to life in a cold place: lion, crocodile, zebra, whale, snake, turtle, giraffe, crab
3 lays eggs: crocodile, snake, turtle, penguin, crab; does not lay eggs: polar bear, lion, zebra, whale, giraffe
4 has a shell: turtle, crab; does not have a shell: polar bear, lion, crocodile, zebra, whale, snake, giraffe, penguin

PAGES 14–15 FOOD CHAINS

Ordering food chains

1 sun, lettuce, caterpillar, thrush
2 sun, seaweed, periwinkle, oystercatcher
3 sun, corn, mouse, cat
4 sun, pondweed, tadpole, duck

Spot the top carnivore!

1 sun, plant buds, monkey, (jaguar)
2 sun, seaweed, fish, seal, (orca)
3 sun, delphinium flower, slug, blackbird, (cat)
4 sun, tree sapling, deer, (wolf)

Who is who?

1 sun, dandelion: **a** (primary producer), snail: **b** (primary consumer), thrush: **c** (secondary consumer), sparrowhawk: **d** (tertiary consumer)

2 sun, primrose: **a** (primary producer), slug: **b** (primary consumer), hedgehog: **c** (secondary consumer), fox: **d** (tertiary consumer)

Predator or prey?

1 cat
2 mountain lion
3 crocodile
4 owl

Missing words

1 energy
2 sun
3 photosynthesis
4 producer
5 herbivore
6 primary
7 carnivores
8 predators

PAGES 16–17 WEB OF LIFE

Choose the right word

1 plants
2 habitat
3 compete
4 adapted
5 carnivores
6 harder

Meanings mix-up!

a 2
b 4
c 3
d 1

Quick questions

1 any such as desert, rainforest, seashore, tundra, garden, wasteland, arctic, etc.
2 fine downy underlayer of feathers, waterproof upper layer thick with greasy lubrication, large leathery feet
3 shell to protect from drying out and predators. Spiky feet for running about on rocks, pincers for extracting food
4 dark Peppered Moth in the city to blend in with grime/dirt from pollution; pale Peppered Moth to blend with less grimy surroundings in the countryside
5 to blend with the snow – for camouflage

Design a creature!

2 suction cups for climbing smooth tree trunks
4 heavy fur to keep out the cold
5 nostril flaps to keep out the smell
6 hammer-shaped bone on the end of the tail with which to break frozen water

Your adaptable pet

1 cat – sharp claws and teeth for killing prey; large canines for tearing meat; good night vision and hearing for hunting
2 rabbit – eyes on the sides of the head for more all-round vision to see predators approaching; large ears and good hearing; fast runner to escape from predators; large back feet for thumping a warning to other rabbits
3 dog – good hearing and sense of smell for hunting; sharp canines for killing prey and tearing meat; large, strong molars for crushing bones
4 hamster – cheek pouches for storing and collecting food to carry to nest; hibernates during long periods of cold weather

PAGES 20–21 INSIDE HUMAN BODIES

Why do you have a skeleton?

a 1 – support: it stops you from flopping about. Your skeleton acts like scaffolding to prop up the soft tissues your body is made from
Example: **e** backbone

b 3 – movement: your bones are rigid, but the joints together with the muscles help us to move about
Example: **f** finger bones

c 2 – protection: hard bony cases that protect your soft internal organs
Example: **d** skull

How the muscles in your arm work

1	biceps	4	triceps
2	muscle	5	relaxes
3	tightens	6	contracts

Quick questions

1 any 5, including: skull, spine, ribs, shin, thighbone, scapula, kneecap, etc.

2 skull

3 elbow, knee

What is inside?

1	brain	5	lungs
2	heart	6	stomach
3	liver	7	kidneys
4	intestine		

Which system is which?

a 4   b 1   c 3   d 2

PAGES 22–23 LOOKING AT TEETH

Which tooth?

1 c – incisor teeth for cutting and cropping grass

2 b – canine teeth for tearing food such as meat

3 a – molars for grinding and chewing food

Quick questions

1 canines

2 molars

3 killing prey/tearing meat

4 bacteria acting on sugars

5 neutralises acid

True or false?

1 T   2 T   3 F   4 F   5 T

Types of teeth and their jobs

1 c   2 b   3 a

Animal detective

1 b   2 a   3 c

PAGES 24–25 HEALTHY OPTIONS

Food groups

a 2

b 1

c 4

d 3

Food group functions

a 4

b 2

c 1

d 3

Choosing healthy options

3 is healthiest because it contains fresh fruit, salad and has a healthy drink. It contains protein – the cheese – but not too much fat or sugar.

1 and **4** contain high levels of fat – pasty, crisps and chocolate biscuit.

2 is a fairly healthy meal but it does contain crisps, which are high in fat, and orange drink, which is high in sugar.

The circulatory system – quick questions

1 arteries

2 arteries

3 artery – flows with high pressure so blood loss would be fast

4 exercise/eat less fatty food

What is blood made up of?

1 c – red cells: these look like red saucers. They carry the dissolved oxygen around the body

2 b – white cells: these attack invading microbes and fight disease

3 d – platelets: these are bits of dead cells. They gum together and help to clot your blood. When you cut yourself, platelets seal the wound to make a scab

4 a – plasma: this is the liquid that contains proteins, salts and sugars

Materials

PAGES 28–29 MATERIALS

Synthetic or natural?

1 a N   b N   c S
   d S   e N   f N

2 a cocoons from silkworms
   b sand
   c wood from trees
   d wool from sheep

Choosing materials

1 not transparent; not weatherproof; not secure (use glass)

2 not weatherproof, strong or secure (use wood, UPVC)

3 too hard (use fabric)

4 breakable (use rigid plastic, wood)

The properties of materials

1 pliable: b, e
   brittle: a, c, d

2 opaque: c, d, e
   transparent: a, b

3 electrical conductors: a, b

Best choice

1 e   2 c   3 b   4 a   5 d

PAGES 30–31 SOLIDS, LIQUIDS AND GASES

Matching descriptions

1 b   2 a   3 c

Solid, liquid or gas?

1 liquid   6 solid
2 solid   7 liquid
3 solid   8 gas
4 gas   9 liquid
5 liquid   10 solid

Changing states

1 state   6 boil
2 solid   7 steam
3 heat   8 gas
4 solid   9 condensed
5 liquid

Reversible changes

1, 3, 4, 5

Reversible or irreversible changes – true or false?

1 F   2 T   3 F   4 F

Quick questions

1 no

2 oxygen, in air

3 liquid

4 gas

5 no – it only flows because it has been ground into tiny crystals. As a large block or crystal it would not flow.

PAGES 32–33 ROCKS AND SOILS

Rock types

1 a – metamorphic – rocks which have been changed by extreme pressure over long periods of time

2 c – igneous – rocks formed from cooled molten lava

3 b – sedimentary – rocks formed by layers of sediment falling to the bottom of the sea, or lakes

Types of soil

1 base   5 cracks
2 pale   6 poor
3 drains   7 plant
4 puddles

The uses of rocks and soils

ticked items are: **1, 2, 4, 6, 7, 8**

Quick questions

1 sedimentary

2 metamorphic

3 it is changed over time by extreme pressure

4 sediment falling to the bottom of the sea/lake over long periods of time

5 molten lava from volcanoes that has cooled rapidly

More quick questions

1 peat

2 clay

3 chalk

4 the rock underneath the soil layer that the soil is made from as the rock breaks down, due to weathering, etc.

5 sandy

PAGES 34–35 KEEPING WARM – INSULATORS

Thermal conductors and insulators

1 a material that allows heat to pass through it easily, such as metal

2 a material that does not allow heat to pass through it easily, such as cork. Thermal insulators are used to keep things warm.

3 metal, water

4 plastic, wood, air

5 metal is a thermal conductor, so it heats up and cooks the food; wood is a thermal insulator, so your hand does not get burnt

Keeping warm

1 insulators   5 cork
2 insulators   6 air
3 air   7 conductor
4 feathers

In the kitchen

1 baking tray   4 metal saucepan
2 hob kettle   5 pottery mug
3 metal spoon

Around the house

Picnic time

Physical processes

PAGES 38–39 FORCES

Quick questions

1 force
2 Newtons
3 N
4 friction
5 it smoothes out the surfaces

Friction action!

1 ice – less friction
2 socks – less friction
3 rough
4 less
5 to grip the road by creating friction

More quick questions

1 friction, air resistance
2 friction
3 upthrust
4 gravity
5 by streamlining the shape

Gravity

1 force
2 gravity
3 pulls
4 down
5 mass
6 strong
7 planets
8 Moon
9 weaker
10 smaller
11 zero
12 float

PAGES 40–41 ELECTRICITY

Electricity flows round a circuit

1 wires
2 battery
3 current
4 circuit
5 electricity
6 switch

Quick questions

1 any – can include: TV, computer, video, lights, cooker, hairdryer, etc.
2 any – can include: games console, remote controlled car, train set, Walkman, etc.
3 it pushes the current through the wire in the same way as a pump pushes water through a pipe
4 solar/fossil fuel power station/hydroelectric/ nuclear/wind turbines, etc.
5 the voltage is high and if something is poked into a wall socket, or wet hands are used on a switch, there is a risk of electric shock

Electricity – true or false?

1 T 2 T 3 F 4 T 5 T

Circuit symbols

1 diagram including ⊣⊢ , ⊗ and ⌐o⌐o
2 diagram including ⊣⊢ , ⊗⊗ and ⌐o⌐o
3 diagram including ⊣⊢ and ⌐⌐
4 diagram including ⊣⊢ and ⊗

PAGES 42–43 SOUND

What do we mean by 'sound'?

1 vibration
2 vibrate
3 vibrations
4 a bones
   b cochlea

Quick questions

1 straight lines
2 oscilloscope
3 amplitude
4 the loudness of a sound
5 decibels
6 dB

Caution – loud noise!

1 to muffle sound and protect the ears
2 yes – but most are treatable if caught early
3 wax, old age
4 you could damage the delicate eardrum
5 no – it generally deteriorates

PAGES 44–45 EARTH AND BEYOND

Day, night and the four seasons

1 T 2 F 3 T 4 T 5 F 6 T 7 T

Missing words

We have day and night and the four seasons, because of the movement of the **1 Earth** as it spins in **2 space**. The Earth **3 orbits** around the sun **4 once** every 365 and a quarter days. This is what we call a **5 year**. The moon takes 28 **6 days** to orbit the Earth. The **7 seasons** are caused by the Earth **8 tilting** over as it turns.

Quick questions

1 the Earth tilting towards or away from the Sun as it turns
2 midday
3 Earth
4 spring, summer
5 longer
6 autumn, winter
7 shorter

Sunrise   Midday   Sunset

More questions

1 No – it is not the Sun that moves; the Earth rotates, making it look as though the Sun is moving across the sky.
2 east
3 midday
4 west
5 at midday as the Sun is at its highest point in the sky
6 early in the morning or late in the afternoon

PAGES 46-47 MAGNETS

Magnet shapes

bar magnet   horseshoe magnet   button magnet

Magnets – true or false?
1 T 2 F 3 T 4 T 5 T 6 F

What materials do magnets attract?
3, 5 – when they are made of iron and steel

they are made from metals (but not all metals are attracted to a magnet)

Attraction and repulsion – magnets
1 attraction
2 repulsion
3 repulsion
4 attraction

Missing words
1 Not all **metals** are attracted to magnets.
2 In fact, most metals are not **attracted** to magnets.
3 **Iron** is attracted to magnets, as is **nickel**.
4 **Cobalt** is also attracted to magnets.
5 **Steel** is a mixture of metals.
6 Steel contains **iron**, so it is attracted to magnets.

PAGES 48–49 LIGHT
Which of these objects are sources of light?
1 Sun   7 fire
3 torch   9 candle
6 lamp

How do we see things?
When **1 light** hits an object, it **2 bounces** off and enters our **3 eyes**. This is how we **4 see** things.

Light travels in straight lines – true or false?
1 T 2 T 3 F 4 F 5 F 6 T

Shadows
1 midday   2 midday   3 east

Transparent, translucent or opaque?
You can see through **1 transparent** materials, such as glass and some plastics. Light can travel through some **2 transparent** materials.

Light can also travel through some **3 translucent** materials, such as frosted glass. You cannot see clearly through **4 translucent** materials.

Light is blocked by **5 opaque** materials. It cannot travel through **6 opaque** materials at all.

Quick questions
1 when an opaque object blocks light
2 shadow
3 move it closer to the light

National Test Practice

PAGES 52–56 NATIONAL TEST PRACTICE
1 ticked boxes are: light, water
2 leaves
3 to anchor it in the ground, draw up water and nutrients from the soil
4 a petal b leaf c stem d root
5 any combination of: animals, birds, wind, water, explosion
6 primary consumers
7 secondary consumer
8 tertiary consumer
9 Sun, dandelion, slug, blackbird, cat
10 They have thick fur and a layer of body fat.
11 ticked boxes are: breathe, move, grow, reproduce
12 a egg, chick, hen b frogspawn, tadpole, frog
   c egg, larva, ladybird
13 a energy b energy stored for use when there are no carbohydrates to burn c builds new cells, for growth and repair
14 a fights disease b carry dissolved oxygen round the body c helps blood to clot; seal wounds with 'scabs'
15 a N, b N, c S, d N, e S
16 sedimentary rock

17 a raw egg to fried egg (I)
   b meringue mixture to cooked meringue (I)
   c cake mixture to cake (I)
   b chocolate block to melted chocolate (R)
   e ice cube to water (R)
18 ticked boxes are: b, d
19 a picture containing battery, bulb (lamp), switch, e.g.

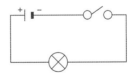

   b it completes the circuit so the electricity can flow round the circuit
   c pencil lead (graphite) and paper clip
20 ticked boxes are: b, c
21 No – shadows are formed when light hits something opaque and cannot 'bend' round it.
22 ticked boxes are: light bulb, torch, candle, fire

Letts and Lonsdale
4 Grosvenor Place
London SW1X 7DL
School orders: 015395 64910
School enquiries: 015395 65921
Parent and student enquiries: 015395 64913
Email: enquiries@lettsandlonsdale.co.uk
Website: www.lettsandlonsdale.com

First published 2007

Editorial and design: 2ibooks [publishing solutions] Cambridge

Colour Reprographics by PDQ

Author: Lynn Huggins-Cooper
Book concept and development: Helen Jacobs, Publishing Director
Project editor: Lily Morgan
Illustrators: Piers Baker and Pumpkin House
Cover design: Angela English

British Library Cataloging in Publication Data. A CIP record of this book is available from the British Library.

9781843157519

The properties of materials

1 Look at the list of materials below. Are they pliable or brittle?

   a moulded plastic   _____

   b rubber tubing   _____

   c glass   _____

   d perspex sheeting   _____

   e fabric   _____

2 Are these materials opaque or transparent?

   a glass   _____

   b polythene sheeting   _____

   c wood   _____

   d stone   _____

   e rubber   _____

3 Are these materials electrical conductors?

   a copper   _____

   b brass   _____

   c polystyrene   _____

   d glass   _____

   e iron   _____

Top Tip *Always try to think about the properties of a material – hard/soft, pliable/brittle, opaque/transparent, conducts heat/does not conduct heat – and how these affect whether it is chosen during the design of an object.*

Best choice

Match the material to the item.

☐ **a** table   **1** aluminium

☐ **b** dress   **2** paper

☐ **c** napkin   **3** fabric

☐ **d** raincoat   **4** wood

☐ **e** saucepan   **5** flexible plastic

Solids, liquids and gases

Matching descriptions

Match the words to the correct description.

1 liquids   **2** solids   **3** gases

☐ **a** Have a definite shape, are quite heavy for their size and do not flow. Think of a brick, for example.

☐ **b** Match the shape of the container they are in and flow easily. Think of a bottle of milk, for example.

☐ **c** Become the same shape of the container they are held in and flow easily. Think of air, for example.

Top Tip

Look around the kitchen and see how many examples of different states of matter you can find. Some, like syrup and sugar, may be hard to classify!

Solid, liquid or gas?

Which state of matter is each substance – a liquid, solid or gas?

1 water _____

2 sugar _____

3 wood _____

4 air _____

5 orange juice _____

6 coal _____

7 syrup _____

8 oxygen _____

9 milk _____

10 salt _____

Changing states

Underline the best word in each pair.

Sometimes we can change the **1** *state / size* of a material. Imagine you have some frozen orange juice. You want to drink it for breakfast, but you cannot because it is a **2** *solid / liquid* lump!

You could **3** *heat / cool* it in the microwave, and change its state. When you first put the block of frozen juice into the microwave, it is a **4** *solid / gas* . As it starts to melt, it changes state into a **5** *gas / liquid* – orange juice. If the juice overheats and the water in it begins to **6** *boil / cool* , it will change state again. As the microwave makes the juice boil, some turns into **7** *steam / carbon dioxide* – the liquid has changed state again and some is now a **8** *gas / solid* (water vapour). If the steam hits the door of the microwave, droplets of water will form. This is where the water vapour has hit a cold surface and **9** *condensed / concentrated* – turned back into a liquid.

Reversible changes

Which of these changes are reversible?

☐ **1** melted chocolate   ☐ **4** melted butter

☐ **2** baked cake mixture   ☐ **5** melted ice

☐ **3** water turned to steam   ☐ **6** wood burnt and turned into ash

Reversible or irreversible changes – true or false?

		True	False
1	Butter heated in a pan changes from a solid to a liquid and cannot be changed back into a solid.	☐	☐
2	Cake mixture baked cannot be turned back into cake mixture.	☐	☐
3	A boiled egg can be turned back from a solid to a liquid.	☐	☐
4	Ash can be changed back into wood.	☐	☐

Quick questions

1 If you made a mug from clay and fired it in a kiln, could you change it back to its pliable original state? _____

2 Which gas do we breathe every day? Where is it found?

_____

3 Is syrup a liquid or a solid? _____

4 Is steam a gas or a liquid? _____

5 Sugar and salt flow. Does that make them liquids? _____

I like solids best - there's chocolate, cake, biscuits, lollies...

But many of them started life as liquids!

Rocks and soils

Rock types

There are three main types of rock. Match the names to the correct description.

1 metamorphic   **2** igneous   **3** sedimentary

☐ **a** Rocks which have been changed by extreme pressure over long periods of time. Examples are: marble, slate.

☐ **b** Rocks formed by layers of sediment falling to the bottom of the sea or lakes. Examples are: sandstone, chalk, limestone. Fossils may be found in these types of rock.

☐ **c** Rocks formed from cooled molten lava. Example: granite.

Types of soil

Fill in the gaps using the words in the box below.

When you think of soil, you probably get a picture in your mind of a dark brown crumbly substance. However, there are many different types of soil in different places. The colour and properties of the soil depend largely upon the **1** _____ rock that the soil is made from. Sandy soil has a **2** _____ colour and water **3** _____ through easily. Clay soil – sticky, orange or blue clay – does not drain easily and **4** _____ lie for some time after rain. It dries out with huge **5** _____ on the surface. Chalky soil has a very pale colour and drains quickly. It is a thin, **6** _____ soil that not many plants are able to grow in. Peat soil is made from ancient, decayed **7** _____ material rather than rock particles. It holds lots of water.

drains   poor   base   cracks   plant   pale   puddles

The uses of rocks and soils

Tick the following building materials which use rock or soil products.

☐ **1** clay pipes   ☐ **2** slates   ☐ **3** plastic guttering

☐ **4** marble fireplaces   ☐ **5** wood   ☐ **6** glass

☐ **7** cement path   ☐ **8** bricks   ☐ **9** iron gate

Electricity – true or false?

		True	False
1	We cannot see electricity, but we can see what it does.	☐	☐
2	Mains electricity can be very dangerous. Nothing should ever be poked in a wall socket.	☐	☐
3	Electricity is stored in a battery and is used up as the battery empties.	☐	☐
4	Electricity is not stored in a battery. Electricity is made or generated inside the battery when the chemicals inside react with one another.	☐	☐
5	When a battery has gone flat, it just means that all the chemicals have reacted with one another.	☐	☐

Mains electricity – the type that we use when we plug things into a socket – can be very dangerous and can kill you if you do not act sensibly. You should never plug things in or touch switches with wet hands or you will get an electric shock. Never poke anything into a plug socket or use appliances with frayed cords for the same reason.

Circuit symbols

Symbols are used by scientists to represent pieces of equipment in a circuit.
Look at the symbols illustrated.

 buzzer battery bulb switch

Draw a circuit that contains:

1 A battery, bulb and an open switch

3 A battery and a buzzer

2 A battery, 2 bulbs and a closed switch

4 A battery and a bulb

Sound

What do we mean by 'sound'?

Underline the best word in each pair to complete the sentences and explain how we hear sound.

1 Sound is a *vibration / explosion* in the air.

2 Imagine you can hear a guitar being played. The sound you hear is made when the strings *move / vibrate* , which causes the air around them to vibrate.

3 The *vibrations / movements* in the air enter your ear and your eardrum vibrates.

4 This in turn makes the tiny *bones / people* inside your ear vibrate. A message is sent through a part of your ear called the *cockleshell / cochlea* through a nerve to your brain, telling you that you can hear guitar music.

Quick questions

1 Does sound travel through the air in wavy lines or in straight lines?

_____

2 Sound waves are invisible, but we can see how they might look with a special instrument. What is it called? _____

3 What does an oscilloscope measure? _____

4 What does 'amplitude' mean? _____

5 What unit is sound measured in? _____

6 What is the symbol for this unit? _____

Mum says I need to get my ears checked by the doctor, because I never hear her calling me.

I'll tell her not to worry - you can hear a sweet paper rustling 100 metres away!

Caution – loud noise!

1   Why do you see people wearing earphones when using tools like pneumatic drills?

_____

2   Can your ears be damaged by infections and illnesses?

_____

3   Name two other ways in which hearing can be affected.

_____

4   Why should you never poke anything in your ears?

_____

5   Does hearing improve as you get older, because you have had more practice at listening?

_____

Try this out

Put an elastic band round a margarine tub. Underneath the tub, between the tub and the elastic band, insert a pencil or pen. Pluck the elastic band and make a sound (when the band vibrates). Then twist the pen once to make the band tighter. Pluck the band again. Is the sound different? Keep tightening the band. What happens to the sound each time you pluck the band? Does the pitch change? Does it get higher or lower?

Write your results here:

Top Tip *We can see light travelling in straight lines clearly at night when we use a torch, see headlights on a car, or the beam of light that shines out of a lighthouse.*

Earth and beyond

Day, night and the four seasons

True or false?

1 We have day and night and the four seasons because of the movement of the Earth as it spins in space. _____

2 We have day and night so we know when to go to sleep. _____

3 The Earth orbits around the Sun once every 365 and a quarter days.

_____

4 The seasons are caused by the Earth tilting over as it turns. _____

5 The seasons are caused by the Moon moving away from the Earth.

_____

6 The Sun rises in the east and sets in the west. _____

7 The Sun is at its highest point at midday. _____

Missing words

Fill in the gaps using the words from the box below.

We have day and night and the four seasons, because of the movement of the **1** _____ as it spins in **2** _____. The Earth **3** _____ around the Sun **4** _____ every 365 and a quarter days. This is what we call a **5** _____. The Moon takes 28 **6** _____ to orbit the Earth. The **7** _____ are caused by the Earth **8** _____ over as it turns.

space   days   tilting   orbits   year   Earth   once   seasons

I like my shadow at midday because it's short and fat!

I like the cat's shadow in the late afternoon – she looks like a long-legged tiger!

Quick questions

1 What causes the seasons? _____

2 During which part of the day is the Sun at its highest in the sky?
_____

3 Is it the Sun or the Earth that moves during the day? _____

4 What season is it in Britain if the north of the Earth is tilted towards the Sun? _____

5 Are the days longer or shorter in summer? _____

6 What season is it in Britain if the north of the Earth is tilted away from the Sun? _____

7 Are the days longer or shorter in winter? _____

Draw the Sun on this picture at sunrise, midday and sunset. Label your drawing.

More questions

1 Does the Sun move across the sky during the day? Explain your answer.
_____
_____

2 As the Sun rises, do we see it in the east or the west? _____

3 When does the Sun appear to be at its highest in the sky? _____

4 Does the Sun seem to 'set' or 'go down' in the east or the west?
_____

5 When do shadows look very short? Explain your answer.
_____

6 When do shadows look very long?
_____

Magnets

Magnet shapes

Magnets come in different shapes. Draw an example in each labelled box.

bar magnet	horseshoe magnet	button magnet

Magnets – true or false?

		True	False
1	Magnets have a north pole and a south pole.	☐	☐
2	Magnets come from the South Pole.	☐	☐
3	If you put the north pole of one magnet next to the south pole of another, the magnets will be attracted to each other and will pull together.	☐	☐
4	If you put two south or north poles together, they will repel and try to push apart from each other.	☐	☐
5	Scientists talk about invisible magnetic fields around magnets.	☐	☐
6	Scientists like to talk about magnets in fields.	☐	☐

I have some great fridge magnets!

I'm just drawn to the fridge like a magnet!

What materials do magnets attract?

Which of the following things are attracted to a magnet?

☐ **1** copper wire

☐ **2** glass bead

☐ **3** drawing pin

☐ **4** jelly sweet

☐ **5** dressmaking pin

☐ **6** tissue

☐ **7** pine cone

☐ **8** plastic toothbrush

What do the things that are attracted to a magnet have in common?

_____

_____

Attraction and repulsion – magnets

Write 'attraction' or 'repulsion' next to each pair of magnets to show what would happen in each case.

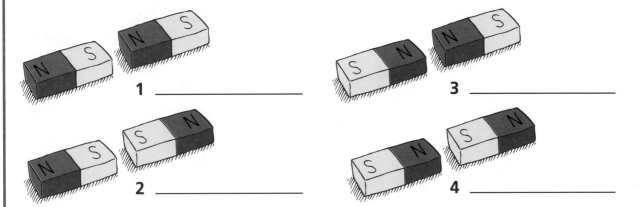

1 _____

2 _____

3 _____

4 _____

Missing words

Fill in the gaps using the words in the box below to help you.

1 Not all m_____ are attracted to magnets.

2 In fact, most metals are **not** a_____ to magnets.

3 I_____ is attracted to magnets, as is n_____.

4 C_____ is also attracted to magnets.

5 S_____ is a mixture of metals.

6 Steel contains i_____, so it is attracted to magnets.

| cobalt | steel | nickel | iron | metals | attracted | iron |

Light

Which of these objects are sources of light?

☐ **1** the Sun ☐ **2** flower ☐ **3** torch ☐ **4** mirror

☐ **5** tin foil ☐ **6** lamp ☐ **7** fire ☐ **8** sequins

☐ **9** candle ☐ **10** moon

How do we see things?

Draw the beam of light from the torch to show how the eye sees the cat.

Then complete the sentences below.

When **1** _____ hits an object, it **2** _____ off and

enters our **3** _____. This is how we **4** _____ things.

Light travels in straight lines – true or false?

	True	False
1 Light travels in straight lines.	☐	☐
2 Since light cannot bend round objects, the light blocked by an object shows up as a shadow.	☐	☐
3 Light travels in invisible wavy lines, like sound waves.	☐	☐
4 Light can bend round corners. We know this because if we look round a door, it is still light.	☐	☐
5 Light beams slide round corners like invisible snakes.	☐	☐
6 When light hits a transparent material, like glass, it can pass through. When it hits an opaque material, like wood, it cannot pass through and a shadow is made.	☐	☐

Quick questions

1 What causes the seasons? ______

2 During which part of the day is the Sun at its highest in the sky?

______

3 Is it the Sun or the Earth that moves during the day? ______

4 What season is it in Britain if the north of the Earth is tilted towards the Sun? ______

5 Are the days longer or shorter in summer? ______

6 What season is it in Britain if the north of the Earth is tilted away from the Sun? ______

7 Are the days longer or shorter in winter? ______

Draw the Sun on this picture at sunrise, midday and sunset. Label your drawing.

More questions

1 Does the Sun move across the sky during the day? Explain your answer.

______

______

2 As the Sun rises, do we see it in the east or the west? ______

3 When does the Sun appear to be at its highest in the sky? ______

4 Does the Sun seem to 'set' or 'go down' in the east or the west?

______

5 When do shadows look very short? Explain your answer.

______

6 When do shadows look very long?

______

Magnets

Magnet shapes

Magnets come in different shapes. Draw an example in each labelled box.

bar magnet	horseshoe magnet	button magnet

Magnets – true or false?

		True	False
1	Magnets have a north pole and a south pole.	☐	☐
2	Magnets come from the South Pole.	☐	☐
3	If you put the north pole of one magnet next to the south pole of another, the magnets will be attracted to each other and will pull together.	☐	☐
4	If you put two south or north poles together, they will repel and try to push apart from each other.	☐	☐
5	Scientists talk about invisible magnetic fields around magnets.	☐	☐
6	Scientists like to talk about magnets in fields.	☐	☐

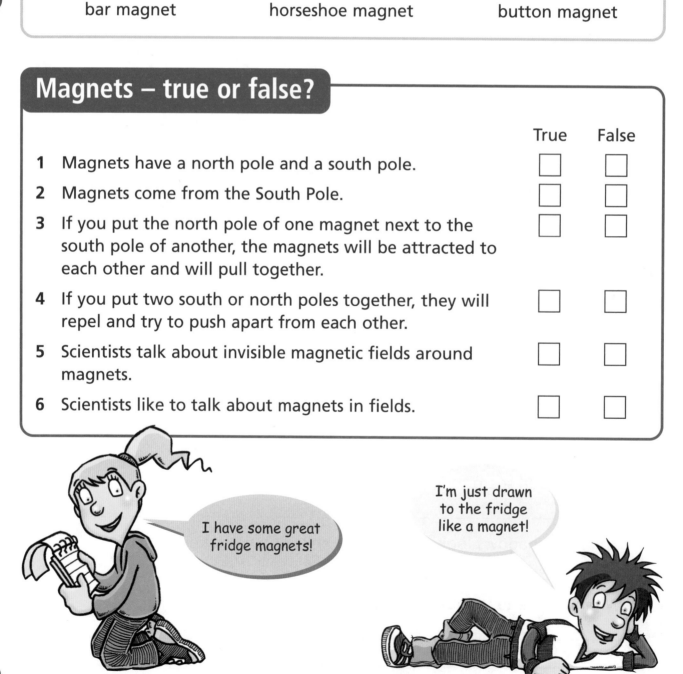

I have some great fridge magnets!

I'm just drawn to the fridge like a magnet!

Shadows

1 When is the Sun at its highest point in the sky?
   (early morning/midday/afternoon)   _____

2 When are shadows at their shortest?
   (early morning/midday/afternoon)   _____

3 Does the Sun rise in the east or west?   _____

Transparent, translucent or opaque?

Choose the correct word – **transparent**, **translucent** or **opaque**. Write the correct word in the boxes.

You can see through **1** _____ materials, such as glass and some plastics. Light can travel through some **2** _____ materials. Light can also travel through some **3** _____ materials, such as frosted glass. You cannot see clearly through **4** _____ materials. Light is blocked by **5** _____ materials. It cannot travel through **6** _____ materials at all.

Quick questions

1 Describe the way in which a shadow is made.

   _____

2 If light is blocked by an object, what is made?

   _____

3 If you made a shadow by holding an object in front of a light source, how could you make it appear larger?

   _____

My favourite source of light is my super hero torch!

Mine is the Sun - because I like playing at the beach!

Physical processes investigation

Can magnets work through other materials?

Can magnets work through other materials?

Investigate the mysterious power of magnetism!

Depending on the strength of the magnet, and the thickness of the materials the magnet is trying to attract a metal object through, magnets can work through other materials.

A magnet can attract an object through paper or card, for example. You can test this by placing paper clips on paper or card and moving them around invisibly from beneath with a magnet.

This ability to attract through other materials can be used to make a spooky haunted house scene where ghosts, furniture, a severed hand (whatever you like!) can move about with no visible intervention... with a little help from your magnet!

What you need

- A cardboard box – make your own using folded out cereal packets
- Paper clips
- Thin card or paper
- Felt pens and scraps for decoration
- A strong magnet from a hobbies or model shop

What to do

1. Make sure your magnet is strong enough to work through your cardboard box. If not, find some thinner card.

2. Decorate the card with scraps and felt pens. Make tiny mirrors with ghoulish reflections, trap doors, cobwebs – let your imagination run riot!

3. Make your moveable objects. They must not be too heavy or they will not move. Try a black spider, a severed hand, a ghost… anything you can think of.

4. Gently draw the magnet along underneath the spider/hand/ghost, through the box, and it should move along by magic!

   You could make other moving scenes such as insects, sea life, cars – whatever you like!

I'm going to use my spooky house at Halloween!

And I'm going to make a moving ghost to scare Mum!

National Test practice

1 What does a plant need to grow? Tick the correct boxes.

☐ light   ☐ water   ☐ soil

☐ cats   ☐ cold   ☐ trowel

2 Which part of a plant uses sunlight to make energy?

_____

3 Why do plants have roots?

_____

_____

4 Label the parts of a flowering plant.

a _____

b _____

c _____

d _____

5 Name four ways in which seeds are dispersed.

_____   _____

_____   _____

6 If the plant is eaten by caterpillars, the caterpillars are:

☐ producers   ☐ primary consumers

☐ secondary consumers   ☐ tertiary consumers

7 If the caterpillars are then eaten by a thrush, the thrush is a:

☐ producer   ☐ primary consumer

☐ secondary consumer   ☐ tertiary consumer

8 If the thrush is eaten by a cat, the cat is a:

☐ producer ☐ primary consumer

☐ secondary consumer ☐ tertiary consumer

9 Put this food chain in order:

dandelion   sun   slug   blackbird   cat

_____

_____

10 How are polar bears adapted to life in the cold?

_____

_____

11 Tick four things that all living things do:

☐ breathe ☐ move ☐ sing ☐ wave

☐ grow ☐ smell ☐ reproduce

12 Put these life cycles in order:

a egg, hen, chick

_____

b tadpole, frogspawn, frog

_____

c ladybird, egg, larva

_____

13 Food groups

a What job do carbohydrates do?

_____

b What job do fats do?

_____

c What does protein do?

_____

14 a What job do white blood cells do?

_____

_____

_____

b What job do red blood cells do?

_____

_____

_____

c What job do platelets do?

_____

_____

_____

15 Synthetic or natural? Put S or N in the boxes.

a feather ☐   **d** pebble ☐

b shell ☐   **e** plastic ☐

c polystyrene ☐

16 In what type of rock are you most likely to find fossils?

_____

17 Reversible or irreversible change?

Put R or I in the boxes.

a raw egg to fried egg ☐

b meringue mixture to cooked meringue ☐

c cake mixture to cake ☐

d chocolate block to melted chocolate ☐

e ice cube to water ☐

18 Tick the magnet combinations that will be attracted to each other.

a ☐   b ☐   c ☐   d ☐

19 Sam and Mel are making a circuit with wire, a battery (cell) and a bulb (lamp). Sam wants to add a switch to turn the bulb on and off.

a Draw a circuit diagram to show how the circuit should be set up.

b Sam closes the switch, and the bulb lights. How does the electricity make the bulb light when the switch is closed?

_____

_____

c Which of these things conduct electricity? Tick the correct boxes.

☐ wooden spoon   ☐ glass jar

☐ pencil lead   ☐ paper bag

☐ sponge block   ☐ paper clip

20 Tick the statements that are true.

a ☐ Electricity is stored in batteries.

b ☐ Mains electricity can be very dangerous.

c ☐ Electricity is made or generated inside a battery when the chemicals inside react with one another.

d ☐ If wires are disconnected from a battery in a circuit, all the electricity will leak away.

21 Can light travel round corners? How do you know?

_____

_____

_____

_____

_____

22 Which of the following things are sources of light? Tick the boxes.

☐ light bulb   ☐ glitter

☐ sequins   ☐ torch

☐ mirror   ☐ candle

☐ tin foil   ☐ fire